TRULY I SAY TO YOU

by Elizabeth Allstrom

woodcuts by Mel Silverman

Abingdon Press   New York   Nashville

Scripture quotations are from the Revised Standard Version of
the Bible, copyrighted 1946 and 1952 by the Division of Christian
Education, National Council of Churches, and are used by per-
mission.

For

Linda, Anne, and Tom

who also are summoned

to try

And Jesus Taught . . .

Seeing the crowds, he went up on the mountain,
and when he sat down his disciples came to him. And he
opened his mouth and taught them, saying . . . .

Matthew 5:1-2

The New Testament passage which begins in this manner is familiar to Christian people everywhere. For at least four centuries it has been known in the English language as the "Sermon on the Mount."

That the mount may be found on no map is of small importance. That the sermon may have been spoken on more than one occasion and in more than one place is of small importance.

Of greater importance are the persons who first heard the sermon, Jesus' disciples and the crowds nearby.

Of greatest importance are the words themselves!

Some are powerful words, striking into minds with such force they cannot be forgotten. Some are winged words, flying like arrows straight to their target and remaining there to rebuke, incite, and disturb. Some are welcome words, bringing gladness to the listeners and directing their lives toward new goals. Some are haunting words, lingering on in memories and bringing new insights and understandings at strange and unexpected times.

For almost twenty centuries the words have called out their message to men and women, boys and girls, challenging each one, "Look closely at your life. What seems of greatest importance to you as you go about your living? Do your thoughts concern only yourself, your interests, your desires? What are the feelings in your heart as you meet the people about you, your friends, your foes?"

And for almost twenty centuries the words have reminded us, "Among the children of God, the real goal of each person's life is to have an awareness of the love that God has for him; and to have a desire and eagerness to do God's work—caring, loving, healing, helping, building—that the world may be truly his."

In Palestine, when the words were first spoken, many sought out Jesus to hear his words. Fishermen left their nets and came to him. Tradesmen left their wares and came. Villagers left the simple tasks within their white, flat-roofed homes and came. Officials left their duties of the moment and came.

Sometimes they found him in the public square or marketplace; sometimes in the cool shade beside the lake or among flowers on a sunny hillside.

Always when Jesus looked out upon those who came, he saw not the crowd but the individuals in it—a mother weary with trying to guide her children in the right way, an old man distraught and discouraged with illness, a child beset by a quick temper, a young man rich, arrogant, selfish. Always as he spoke to them, he talked not to the crowd but to the individuals in it.

"Truly, I say to you...." Jesus introduced his listeners to a new world whose very existence had been unknown to them, a world of a loving God in whom they could put their trust. He showed them a God who cares equally for every person, who has a plan for each life in a world that those, with love in their hearts, can help to make.

In his teaching Jesus held no book in his hands, yet all who heard him sensed something amazing, something startling and new, in what he said. Some, curious and wondering at what they heard, shared their thoughts with no one. Others spoke out and tried to annoy and confuse Jesus with their questions. Others, accepting and believing, held his words in their hearts to become a guide for their daily thoughts and actions.

The common folk felt in his statements such a compassion for them and their lot, such an understanding of their troubles, that they listened freely and gladly. One to another they said, "This man teaches as one who has authority."

. . . About Happiness

Blessed are the poor in spirit, for theirs is the kingdom of heaven.

Blessed are those who mourn, for they shall be comforted.

Blessed are the meek, for they shall inherit the earth.

Blessed are those who hunger and thirst for righteousness, for they shall be satisfied.

Blessed are the merciful, for they shall obtain mercy.

Blessed are the pure in heart, for they shall see God.

Blessed are the peacemakers, for they shall be called sons of God.

Blessed are those who are persecuted for righteousness' sake, for theirs is the kingdom of heaven.

Blessed are you when men revile you and persecute you and utter all kinds of evil against you falsely on my account, Rejoice and be glad, for your reward is great in heaven, for so men persecuted the prophets who were before you.

Matthew 5:3-12

On the day that Jesus talked about the blessed ones, he suggested, "Happiness comes from within your heart. It is not the result of money or other possessions. It is the result of the way you live and think." Such thoughts no doubt seemed strange and incredible to all the listeners. Yet to many they were like jets of light and hope. For under the harsh authority of their Roman rulers many had known only dark and joyless days, days filled with much hardship and little happiness. And they wanted happiness.

Jesus' words gave them something to lean on. With new expectancy they must have thought, "Perhaps for us happiness is not just an absurd dream. Perhaps it is within our reach after all."

"Give up your pride," Jesus told his listeners. "Give up your desire for popularity. Such things do not make you strong within or bring you a greater happiness. They keep you away from God, your Father. He is found when your heart is humble. And then, when you find him, oh, the happiness you will know!"

He told them too, "Be sorry about your wrongdoings, your selfish ways. Be sorry and seek forgiveness. Only then will you begin to see the purpose that God has for your life—that you put the good of others before your own. And then, working to achieve this, oh, the happiness you will know!"

Jesus described still other changes that each listener must make in his life if he would know true happiness. "If you are anxious about the troubles and problems of a future day, if you are provoked, annoyed, or hurt by words another might say about you, remember that you cannot help or change these things. Be confident and happy because God's love surrounds you every day. And then, never forgetting this, oh, the happiness you will know!

"Show justice and mercy to all persons, friend and foe alike. Be generous to all. Seek to become closer to God, so that knowing his will for you, you may let the feelings of your heart direct your actions. And then, oh, the happiness you will know!

"Love builds. Hate destroys. Therefore, fill your life with so much love, good will, and thoughtful deeds toward others that there is no room for hate and revenge. Never expect another to do these kindly deeds in your place. No, you must do them yourself. And then, oh, the happiness you will know!

"Serve God with courage. Serve him with a single purpose. In so serving you will increase the amount of love that is at work in the world. And then, oh, the happiness you will know!

"Reproach and scorn always have been the lot of the servant. But become God's servant. Rejoice in any work that you can do for him. Stand always for what you believe to be right. Then accept gladly, without fuss or protest, any reproach or scorn the world may hurl at you. And then, oh, the happiness you will know!"

. . . About Sharing One's Self

You are the salt of the earth; but if salt has lost its taste, how shall its saltness be restored? It is no longer good for anything except to be thrown out and trodden under foot by men.

You are the light of the world. A city set on a hill cannot be hid. Nor do men light a lamp and put it under a bushel, but on a stand, and it gives light to all in the house. Let your light so shine before men, that they may see your good works and give glory to your Father who is in heaven.

Matthew 5:13-16

19

In his thirty years of looking, listening, living, learning, Jesus had come to know and understand the people around him. He knew their goodness. He knew also their pettiness and their meanness. Yet he had confidence that each life

could have a fresh meaning, that all its admirable traits
could be directed toward a new purpose, if only the person
in his day-by-day living would permit it. In his teaching he
would try to help each listener to believe that his best self

21

was a worthy self, and that being worthy it could become an example for others. Yes! He would teach this lesson with word pictures of simple objects used daily in every home.

He would compare his listeners to salt. Salt! A word not easily forgotten. No home was without salt. It was a necessary seasoning. Even the smallest children knew the importance of salt, knew that without salt food was flat and tasteless.

He would compare his listeners to light. Light! A word not easily forgotten. Every family knew from experience the brightness of the light cast from the wick burning in their small clay lamp. When the lamp was placed in the niche in the wall, its light filled all the room, driving shadows away, bringing brightness and cheer to every corner. When it was placed in the small window, its beam shone out across the path and beyond, guiding members of the family safely home and directing unknown travelers along their way.

So Jesus spoke out to the people. "You are the salt of the earth," he said. "A pinch of salt seems small, yet a small amount can flavor a whole meal. Just so your goodness can flavor your world. It is the seasoning that no one but you can give. Salt that is without flavor is not good. Neither is your world good unless it has your gifts of gentleness, goodness, earnestness, loyalty. So give them freely that others, seeing, may be influenced by them. To do this is your duty and your joy.

"You are the light of the world." Jesus' second challenge was even stronger, perhaps, than his first. "A light that blesses must not be concealed. Do not hide your kindness, your humanness. Let them become like beams of light shining afar, even to the ends of the earth, touching other lives and blessing them. It is your light that may reveal to them the hope of what they may become, of the kind of world they may help to build. Hold your beam high! Never hide its shining. Live always at your best, so that the light of your life may guide all who see it."

. . . About the Old Law

and the New Law

Think not that I have come to abolish the law and the prophets; I have come not to abolish them but to fulfil them. For truly, I say to you, till heaven and earth pass away, not an iota, not a dot, will pass from the law until all is accomplished.

Whoever then relaxes one of the least of these commandments and teaches men so, shall be called least in the kingdom of heaven; but he who does them and teaches them shall be called great in the kingdom of heaven. For I tell you, unless your righteousness exceeds that of the scribes and Pharisees, you will never enter the kingdom of heaven.

25

You have heard that it was said to the men of old, "You shall not kill; and whoever kills shall be liable to judgment." But I say to you that every one who is angry with his brother shall be liable to judgment; whoever insults his brother shall be liable to the council, and whoever says, "You fool!" shall be liable to the hell of fire. So if you are offering your gift at the altar, and there remember that your brother has something against you, leave your gift there before the altar and go; first be reconciled to your brother, and then come and offer your gift. Make friends quickly with your accuser, while you are going with him to court, lest your accuser hand you over to the judge, and the judge to the guard, and you be put in prison; truly, I say to you, you will never get out till you have paid the last penny.

You have heard that it was said, "You shall not commit adultery." But I say to you that every one who looks at a woman lustfully has already committed adultery with her in his heart. If your right eye causes you to sin, pluck it out and throw it away; it is better that you lose one of your members than that your whole body be thrown into hell. And if your right hand causes you to sin, cut it off and throw it away; it is better that you lose one of your members than that your whole body go into hell.

It was also said, "Whoever divorces his wife, let him give her a certificate of divorce." But I say to you that every one who divorces his wife, except on the ground of unchastity, makes her an adulteress; and whoever marries a divorced woman commits adultery.

Again you have heard that it was said to the men of old, "You shall not swear falsely, but shall perform to the Lord what you have sworn." But I say to you, Do not swear at all, either by heaven, for it is the throne of God, or by the earth, for it is his footstool, or by Jerusalem, for it is the city of the great King. And do not swear by your head, for you cannot make one hair white or black. Let what you say be simply "Yes" or "No"; anything more than this comes from evil.

You have heard that it was said, "An eye for an eye and a tooth for a tooth." But I say to you, Do not resist one who is evil. But if any one strikes you on the right cheek, turn to him the other also; and if any one would sue you and take your coat, let him have your cloak as well; and if any one forces you to go one mile, go with him two miles. Give to him who begs from you, and do not refuse him who would borrow from you.

You have heard that it was said, "You shall love your neighbor and hate your enemy." But I say to you, Love your enemies and pray for those who persecute you, so that you may be sons of your Father who is in heaven; for he makes his sun rise on the evil and on the good, and sends rain on the just and on the unjust. For if you love those who love you, what reward have you? Do not even the tax collectors do the same? And if you salute only your brethren, what more are you doing than others? Do not even the Gentiles do the same? You, therefore, must be perfect, as your heavenly Father is perfect.

Matthew 5:17-48

Jesus knew the good and evil thoughts that the people carried hidden in their imaginations. Yet he was confident that the good thoughts could erase the evil ones if only each person would look deep inside himself and examine the motives for his actions, and then begin to accept responsibility for those actions.

Jesus wanted to help his hearers understand the difference between a life which followed rigidly the old laws, spoken long ago to the people by Moses, and a life striving openly to follow God's laws of the spirit.

He would help them to see that God demands that a

man be transformed from within, that he become a new being with his every thought, word, and deed; that he be able to recognize the right in every situation and be ready to respond to it in the right way even with no other person nearby to direct him.

Now in his teaching Jesus spoke out in a manner something like this: "You know well the words of the old laws that came long ago to your fathers from God through Moses, 'There shall be no murder.' 'There shall be no adultery.' Truly, I say to you, you must have mastery over all your feelings and desires. Let your heart know no anger at any time. Let no impure thoughts of any kind creep into it. Train yourself always to think good of a person because good is there. When you seek it you will find it."

Next, Jesus recalled for his listeners the old law regarding divorce, "You remember how Moses said, 'If a man wants to send his wife away—to divorce her—he must go through the regular legal process.' "

Jesus knew that they indeed remembered, for in those ancient times when the law was given by Moses, a wife often was considered to be very much like a slave; whenever a husband wished to be divorced from her he needed only to notify the authorities that he no longer claimed her in this role, and the divorce was made legal.

Continuing, Jesus might well have directed the listeners' thoughts not to further comments about the law's

requirements for securing a divorce, but to a description of a marriage partnership where a divorce would never be necessary. "Truly, I say to you, when any one of you, with another person, decide that you want to be partners together in creating a home and family, approach such a decision with deliberateness and assurance. Show no haste. Be confident that the chosen partner is a person worthy to receive your love, a person to whom you happily can give your love for the whole of your lifetime. Then, give it to this person, and to no other, for as long as you both shall live."

As to the taking of oaths, Jesus declared, "In the old law if you take an oath and claim that you are promising both God and man that you will do thus and so, then you must do what you have promised. But I say to you that a simple 'Yes' promised by a trustworthy man is of more value than a complicated statement legally sworn to by a cheat and a deceiver. In truth, if every person were completely trustworthy there would be no need for legal guarantees."

He then brought to his listeners' remembrance another old law, "An eye for an eye; a tooth for a tooth," and proceeded to explain the action he required in response to it. "Truly, I say to you that to pay back in the same manner for whatever wrong has been done to you causes only more resentment, more bitterness. Neither person is benefited.

31

Revenge gained by returning evil for evil is not sweet. It is like a poison and it harms both persons. Instead of seeking revenge from your enemy, forgive him. In doing this, you yourself become free.

"Give more than is asked of you. Do more than is asked. Yes, even walk the second mile. When, on the first mile, you are forced to carry the pack of a Roman soldier, do so in obedience to the law of Caesar, your ruler. But when by your own choice you carry the pack for a second mile and meet the despised law with kindness, you are obeying the law of God, your Father."

Again Jesus directed his listeners to think of another of the old laws. "You remember well the words of the old law that commands, 'Love your neighbor.' Truly, I say to you that all men are your neighbors and brothers, both friends and enemies alike. All of you are children of God. Therefore, care about all men. Seek good for all men, both loved ones and hated ones. Be impartial in your love even as God is impartial. God's sun shines alike on the good and the evil. His rain falls equally on the just and unjust. Let your love be like that, free and complete for every person. If you love only those who love you, you gain but little."

One can imagine the reactions of the listeners. Some of the crowd may have frowned or spoken out in anger and outrage. How dare this teacher put his finger on the spot in their lives that could not bear such examination?

Perhaps some, feeling unable to measure up to these words, stretched out their arms in despair.

Some, unwilling to acknowledge the inner motives that guided their actions, must have been frightened.

Others, wishing not to be tested further, may have walked away.

Still others, though realizing the difficulties and the hardships they must face in obeying the new law, accepted it as the way of life to which they would give their allegiance. Their minds at ease, they waited to hear more.

"Waste no time," Jesus urged. "Begin now to aim your life toward the perfection of God, your Father. Just as God works quietly without show or pomp, so you must work quietly, needing neither praise nor applause for what you do, but letting the roots of your life go deep that they may hold you strong and erect.

"Just as God works faithfully, giving his hours, days, and seasons in dependable regularity, so must you work faithfully to bring about the right and good. These do not come by chance but because someone works to give them life.

"Just as God is fair and equitable, giving the same hardships, the same good gifts, and the same love to all men alike, so must you be fair and just. Always show the same self to those who come to you—not a kindly manner to some, a rude and insulting manner to others."

33

One can imagine the listeners that day returning to their homes and work—the peasants and learned ones, the lowly and influential ones, the youthful and elderly ones. Jesus' pictures were fixed in their minds whether they wanted them there or not: *"Salt!* You are the salt . . ." and *"Light!* You are the light. . . ." His words were ringing in their ears whether they wanted to hear them or not. "Let your heart know no anger at any time. . . . Give more than is asked of you. . . . Love your enemy. . . . Aim your life toward the perfection of your Father. . . ."

And their own questions pounded in their hearts, whether they would acknowledge them or not: Can I really make my world better? Can my life become a light to guide another? Dare I begin now, this very day, to examine my inner self? Can I search out the motives that direct what I do? If I try can I really begin to catch the spirit of God's goodness? Can I follow in his way?

. . . About Worship

Beware of practicing your piety before men in order to be seen by them; for then you will have no reward from your Father who is in heaven.

Thus, when you give alms, sound no trumpet before you, as the hypocrites do in the synagogues and in the streets, that they may be praised by men. Truly, I say to you, they have their reward. But when you give alms, do not let your left hand know what your right hand is doing, so that your alms may be in secret; and your Father who sees in secret will reward you.

And when you pray, you must not be like the hypocrites; for they love to stand and pray in the synagogues and at the street corners, that they may be seen by men. Truly, I say to you, they have their reward. But when you pray, go into your room and shut the door and pray to your Father who is in secret; and your Father who sees in secret will reward you.

And in praying do not heap up empty phrases as the Gentiles do; for they think that they will be heard for their many words. Do not be like them, for your Father knows what you need before you ask him. Pray then like this:

> Our Father who art in heaven,
> Hallowed be thy name.
> Thy kingdom come,
> Thy will be done,
>   On earth as it is in heaven.
> Give us this day our daily bread;
> And forgive us our debts,
>   As we also have forgiven our
>   debtors;
> And lead us not into temptation,
>   But deliver us from evil.

For if you forgive men their trespasses, your heavenly Father also will forgive you; but if you do not forgive men their trespasses, neither will your Father forgive your trespasses.

And when you fast, do not look dismal, like the hypocrites, for they disfigure their faces that their fasting may be seen by men. Truly, I say to you, they have their reward. But when you fast, anoint your head and wash your face, that your fasting may not be seen by men but by your Father who is in secret; and your Father who sees in secret will reward you.

Matthew 6:1-18

When Jesus spoke out against the religious practices of the times, he spoke as one well qualified to do so. As a boy, had not his keen eyes observed well the religious customs of those around him? Had not his keen mind remembered well the laws and rules learned at home and in synagogue school?

On this day he may have begun his teaching with this startling statement: "Your religion is not something to be worn on your sleeve for the eyes of men to see." And to have followed it, sermon fashion, with descriptions of three of their common practices which pointed out their lack of sincerity and honesty in worship.

"When you come to the temple bringing your gifts for others," Jesus reminded them, "you sound a trumpet as if publicly to announce, 'Look, everyone! Notice that the alms I bring for the Lord are of precious gold, while yours of common silver and copper are of much less value.' Truly, I say to you that God looks upon all gifts alike. Do your good works without show. Indeed, one of your hands need not know what the other one does.

"When you worship in the temple, you speak aloud your high-sounding phrases as if to announce, 'Listen, everyone! I now recite my prayers before you that you may be impressed by my reverence, by my upright and devout character.' Truly, I say to you that such prayer is of no value. Prayer is the means by which you communicate with God, though he knows your thoughts before you speak

them. You need not use unusual words, but speak to him in prayer as you would to an honored and loved earthly father.

"When you fast you let your unwashed face and unkempt garments call attention to yourself as if to announce, "See, everyone! These signs are proof to you that I am indeed a pious and godly man.' Truly, I say to you that your fasting and all your good works are not for the eyes of men. They are for God's eyes alone. Their purpose is to glorify and serve God, not to call attention to yourself."

When Jesus went on to talk about prayer as a means of worship, he wanted the people to see that the prayer he gave them was to be a guide for all prayer. It was a prayer to be repeated thoughtfully. It could be made at any time for one needs no regular hour or day to speak with God.

Jesus wanted them to see, too, that his prayer applied to all persons, not just to a chosen few, and that each time its words were repeated, the one at prayer must thoughtfully reexamine himself and try then, even harder than before, to live in accordance with the thoughts expressed.

Perhaps to the people that day Jesus explained, "Begin your prayer with the words, 'Our Father, . . . hallowed be thy name.' In repeating these words you acknowledge that God rules both your life and all life. You acknowledge also brotherhood to all men, and as a brother to every man you accept an obligation to every man.

"When you say, 'Thy kingdom come, thy will be done,'

you are saying that you and all persons—the farmer at his planting, the sandal maker at his bench, the baker at his mixing trough, the musician at his lute, the child at his play—must learn to do God's will and, with rejoicing, must direct your activity to his glory.

"The words 'daily bread' are a constant reminder that you and all persons are dependent on God's goodness for your needs. God, not you, commands the sun, wind, rain, planting time, and harvest time. But you are not to sit idly, waiting to receive God's gifts. You who expect to receive his bounty must exert your own effort and thought.

" 'Forgive us our debts as we forgive our debtors' calls to your mind that both a deed done and one left undone may be causes for seeking your Father's forgiveness. If either is left unforgiven, the closeness between you is gone. This is not good. Nor is it good when you, with an unforgiving spirit in your heart, permit doubt and mistrust to creep between you and a friend, separating you.

"In the words, 'Lead us not into temptation,' you recognize that common weaknesses have not passed you by. You, too, possess faults, and they may lead you into trouble at any time. Yet you are not required to meet the difficulties alone. Needed strength will come to you from your Father.

"In making the petition, 'Deliver us from evil,' never forget that he also will help you to meet the world's evils and to take action against them. They are all around you. You cannot escape them."

43

... About Anxiety

Do not lay up for yourselves treasures on earth, where moth and rust consume and where thieves break in and steal, but lay up for yourselves treasures in heaven, where neither moth nor rust consumes and where thieves do not break in and steal. For where your treasure is, there will your heart be also.

The eye is the lamp of the body. So, if your eye is sound, your whole body will be full of light; but if your eye is not sound, your whole body will be full of darkness. If then the light in you is darkness, how great is the darkness!

No one can serve two masters; for either he will hate the one and love the other, or he will be devoted to the one and despise the other. You cannot serve God and mammon.

Therefore I tell you, do not be anxious about your life, what you shall eat or what you shall drink, nor about your body, what you shall put on. Is not life more than food, and the body more than clothing? Look at the birds of the air: they neither sow nor reap nor gather into barns, and yet your heavenly Father feeds them. Are you not of more value than they? . . . And why are you anxious about clothing? Consider the lilies of the field, how they grow: they neither toil nor spin; yet I tell you, even Solomon in all his glory was not arrayed like one of these. But if God so clothes the grass of the field, which today is alive and tomorrow is thrown into the oven, will he not much more clothe you, O men of little faith? Therefore do not be anxious, saying, "What shall we eat?" . . . or "What shall we wear?" For the Gentiles seek all these things; and your heavenly Father knows that you need them all. But seek first his kingdom and his righteousness, and all these things shall be yours as well.

Therefore, do not be anxious about tomorrow, for tomorrow will be anxious for itself. Let the day's own trouble be sufficient for the day.

Matthew 6:19-34

As a boy in synagogue school Jesus had learned the
Great Law, "Hear, O Israel: The Lord our God is one

Lord; and you shall love the Lord your God with all your heart, and with all your soul, and with all your might." At home the treasured words of the law were safely held in a mezuzah on the doorpost. He and his family, going in and out through the doorway, had touched the little box countless times, had repeated the words from memory and felt God's nearness.

At play on the hills of Nazareth Jesus had known the spacious world of God's creation. He had watched birds building their nests, darting here and there, finding food for their young. He had heard their chatter, their joyous songs as they worked. How naturally these small creatures went about their business of living! How wonderful the gift of life they had received from God, the Father!

On the hillsides Jesus had watched growing lilies, the wild poppies of the East. How relaxed the flowers were as they danced and swayed in the breeze. They seemed to have not a single care or responsibility, no spinning to do at the wheel as Mary did, no toiling to do at the carpenter's bench as Joseph did. How bright their colors, even brighter and more beautiful than those in the robes of Solomon, the king!

Through the years such childhood experiences remained fresh in the mind of Jesus, the teacher, and one day he used them in his teaching.

"In your life," Jesus said, "you cannot journey along two paths, thinking one day of your easy living, your personal possessions, thinking another day of the service and good will you plan for others. No! You must decide on one path or the other.

"If you strive for money and other outward possessions and think only of them, these puny treasures will govern your life. Such things are easily lost, stolen, or destroyed. If you hold on to the things of the heart—thoughtfulness of others, kindly deeds, happiness of those around you—and think only of them, these become the treasures that will guide your life. Thieves cannot steal these treasures. Nor can they be lost or destroyed."

But there was something even more important that he must make clear to his hearers. "When you depend on outward possessions for your happiness and security," Jesus said, "you are putting God second in your life. Truly, I say to you that you must put God first, serving him with all your heart, soul, and might, not with half. When you give him your total loyalty, you will have no anxiety about the morrow, what you shall eat and wear, how the inch is added to your stature, the day to your span of life. Love and trust in him overcome all anxiety.

"Without worry, you then are free to adapt to God's way for your life as truly as the birds and flowers adapt to his way for their lives. You then can do useful work in the world, mastering today's problems, doing well today's tasks.

"Such work is your preparation for meeting with full confidence the unforeseen of the morrow.

"Seek, therefore, the path that leads to God. Trust in him. Through him let strength and meaning come into your life, filling it with a glowing. Without this inner light your days will be meaningless—your life will know only a great gloom."

... About Making Judgments

Judge not, that you be not judged. For with the judgment you pronounce you will be judged, and the measure you give will be the measure you get. Why do you see the speck that is in your brother's eye but do not notice the log that is in your own eye? Or how can you say to your brother, "Let me take the speck out of your eye," when there is the log in your own eye? You hypocrite, first take the log out of your own eye, and then you will see clearly to take the speck out of your brother's eye.

51

Do not give dogs what is holy; and do not throw your pearls before swine, lest they trample them underfoot and turn to attack you.

Ask, and it will be given you; seek, and you will find; knock, and it will be opened to you. For every one who asks receives, and he who seeks finds, and to him who knocks it will be opened. Or what man of you, if his son asks him for a loaf, will give him a stone? Or if he asks for a fish, will give him a serpent? If you then, who are evil, know how to give good gifts to your children, how much more will your Father who is in heaven give good things to those who ask him? So whatever you wish that men would do to you, do so to them; for this is the law and the prophets.

Enter by the narrow gate; for the gate is wide and the way is easy, that leads to destruction, and those who enter by it are many. For the gate is narrow and the way is hard, that leads to life, and those who find it are few.

Beware of false prophets, who come to you in sheep's clothing but inwardly are ravenous wolves. You will know them by their fruits. Are grapes gathered from thorns, or figs from thistles? So, every sound tree bears good fruit, but the bad tree bears evil fruit. A sound tree cannot bear evil fruit, nor can a bad tree bear good fruit. Every tree that does not bear good fruit is cut down and thrown into the fire. Thus you will know them by their fruits.

Not every one who says to·me, "Lord, Lord," shall enter the kingdom of heaven, but he who does the will of

my Father who is in heaven. On that day many will say to me, "Lord, Lord, did we not prophesy in your name, and cast out demons in your name, and do many mighty works in your name?" And then will I declare to them, "I never knew you; depart from me, you evildoers."

Every one then who hears these words of mine and does them will be like a wise man who built his house upon the rock; and the rain fell, and the floods came, and the winds blew and beat upon that house, but it did not fall, because it had been founded on the rock. And every one who hears these words of mine and does not do them will be like a foolish man who built his house upon the sand; and the rain fell, and the floods came, and the winds blew and beat against that house, and it fell; and great was the fall of it.

Matthew 7:1-28

Again and again in observing the people around him, Jesus had noticed the many sorrows and hurts that came into lives because of hasty and unjust judgments made against them, intolerant attitudes held against them, narrow and critical opinions expressed against them.

He could but wonder, "Have those who caused such sorrow and hurt so easily forgotten the essentials of my teaching—that one man is another man's brother, that each must be concerned for his brother's well-being? Have they so quickly let slip from their minds the demands made upon them by the spirit of God's law—to forgive, to love, to aim one's life toward the perfection of God?"

He could but plan, "Those who hear my teaching must be warned again of the destruction that lies ahead for those who are hearers only. They must be reminded again of the hardships and also the rewards that await those who both hear the teaching and follow it."

And again he used illustrations from his listeners' experiences. Everyone had felt the beating rains and blowing winds and had stood on sands that crumbled beneath them. A speck in the eye, a narrow gate, a house built on a rock were common sights to most of his hearers. To these he would add others—absurd, impossible situations that, by chance, might bring a smile—a wolf appearing in sheep's clothing, grapes gathered from thorns, good fruit found on bad trees.

Again Jesus must have startled his hearers: "Truly, I say to you that every man, each one of you, is fighting some kind of battle. Yet you show neither mercy nor kindness in the criticisms and judgments you hurl against each other. Every man, each one of you, has his own weaknesses, his own failings, yet you do not correct your own before you call attention to those in another. Yes! I say to you, examine yourself carefully lest your own pride, your own defenses, make you blind to the very wrongs within yourself that you think you see so clearly in another."

"And," he continued, "do not be foolish or unreasonable in what you try to do in my name. If those with whom you try to share the message of God's love give no response to it, if they scorn it, or know not its value, it is futile and wasteful for you to continue. Every man is the keeper of God's gifts. He holds them in his hand, and to treat with scorn treasures that God has given, and that man can never replace, is wrong.

"God's love for you is greater than that any earthly father shows to the son he loves. No father whose son asks for bread gives a stone. He gives good gifts. Good gifts from your Father are within your reach if you but seek them and ask for them. The measure of what you may ask from him is the measure of what you do for another."

Jesus left no doubt about how this was to be done. "If you want to know what to do for another, you have but to imagine yourself in that person's place. Consider his wants. Become aware of his needs. Then do these things for him accordingly."

He left no doubt about the outcome of men's lives—those built on the solid rock of brotherhood and love and those built on the shifting sands of self. "Selfishness and indulgence separate you from God," he said. "Such a life is easy. It is entered by a wide gate. Many go through it.

"Generosity and thoughtfulness in the service of others bring you into God's presence. Such a life is not easy. It is entered by a narrow gate. Few go through it.

"Like a tree that is judged by the fruit of its branches, you too, are judged. Do you gather good fruit from a tree that is not sound? Do you come with a sharing heart or a selfish heart? Do you help or harm? Do you seek to serve or to be served? Truly, I say to you that your good works do not make you good, but if you are good you will do good works.

"You do not prove your earnestness by calling out, 'Lord! Lord!' No, you prove it by your eagerness to do God's will. So hear my words and follow them. When you do this you are building your life on a solid rock. Though the rains and winds of fear, doubt, and self-reproach beat and blow against this life with great force, it will stand strong and firm. On such a foundation your life will know great happiness.

"If you hear my words and yet continue to let your actions be directed by your outward possessions, you are building your life on sand. When these same rains and winds beat and blow against this life, the sands will crumble beneath it. This life will topple. In its fall there will be great sadness."

And Crowds Followed Him

> And when Jesus finished these sayings, the crowds were astonished at his teaching, for he taught them as one who had authority, and not as their scribes.
>
> When he came down from the mountain, great crowds followed him.
>
> *Matthew 7:29, 8:1*

In the nearly two thousand years from that long-ago day to the present, great crowds have continued to follow Jesus, the teacher. The words that first were spoken by him to his disciples and the crowds nearby—powerful words, winged words, welcome words, haunting words—have

61

continued to cling in memories, have continued to call out
their challenge to men and women, boys and girls:

> Examine your life!
> Let it be one whose purpose is worthy
>   of him who spoke the words;
> Let it be one bearing fruit that is good;
> Let it be one that pushes selfishness
>   aside;
> Let it be one gladly accepting responsi-
>   bility for the happiness and well-being
>   of others;
> Let it be one following the spirit of God's
>   law, accepting all men as brothers and
>   neighbors.

The words continue to cause old and young, wherever their home, whatever their faith, whatever their occupation, to wonder and to seek answers to their wonderings:

> Can I really follow these hard commands of
>   Jesus?
> Is my happiness really to be found in the
>   in the way he suggests?
> Can my brief life really add seasoning
>   and light in a world already filled
>   with the seasoning and light of so
>   many others?

Yes! Jesus' hard commands set a high standard for each life. It demands complete and total loyalty to him. To follow it is never easy. Yet, like those on the mount who heard them first, those who hear the words today are summoned to try. They, too, have the assurance of God's love, the promise of his guidance and strength.